AND ALL THAT JAZZ
from CHICAGO

Words by FRED EBB
Music by JOHN KANDER

Copyright © 1973, 1975 by Unichappell Music Inc. and Kander & Ebb, Inc.
Copyright Renewed
All Rights Administered by Unichappell Music Inc.
International Copyright Secured   All Rights Reserved

strat - o - sphere,__ how could he lend an ear __ to all

if she'd hear ____ her ba - by's queer __ for all

that jazz? _____

that jazz.) _____

BUT THE WORLD GOES 'ROUND

from NEW YORK, NEW YORK

Music by JOHN KANDER
Lyrics by FRED EBB

© 1977 (Renewed) UNITED ARTISTS CORPORATION
All Rights Controlled and Administered by EMI UNART CATALOG INC. (Publishing) and ALFRED PUBLISHING CO., INC. (Print)
All Rights Reserved   Used by Permission

CABARET
from the Musical CABARET

Words by FRED EBB
Music by JOHN KANDER

Copyright © 1966, 1967 by Alley Music Corp. and Trio Music Company
Copyright Renewed
International Copyright Secured   All Rights Reserved
Used by Permission

CITY LIGHTS

from THE ACT

Words by FRED EBB
Music by JOHN KANDER

Copyright © 1978 by Unichappell Music Inc. and Kander & Ebb, Inc.
All Rights Administered by Unichappell Music Inc.
International Copyright Secured   All Rights Reserved

egg that the hen just laid." The

Slower, with freedom

lit - tle old la - dy took off her glass - es and squint - ed,

and how she re - spond - ed lit - ter - al - ly had me

floored. She said, It's nice to meet some - one who ap -

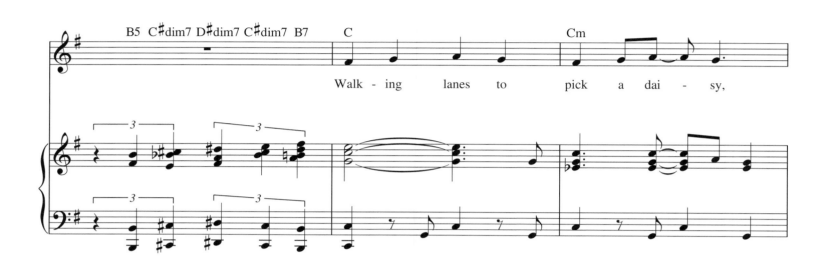

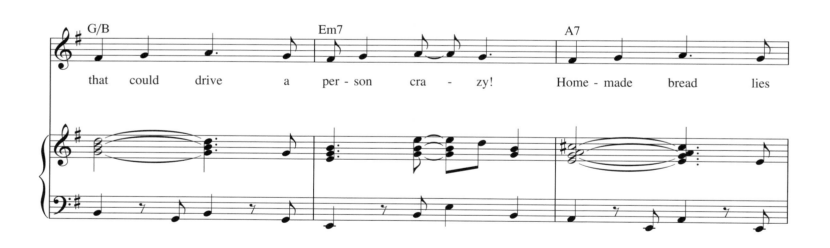

Walk-ing lanes to pick a dai - sy,

that could drive a per-son cra - zy! Home-made bread lies

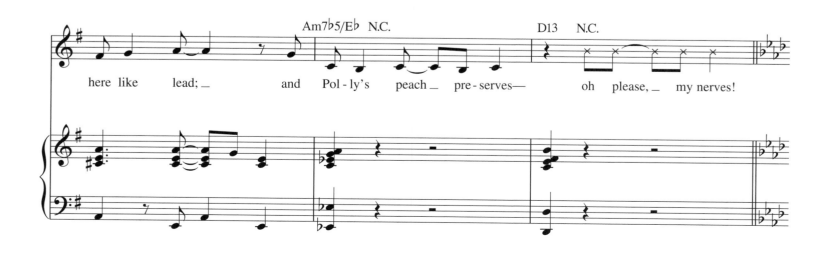

here like lead; __ and Pol-ly's peach __ pre-serves— oh please, __ my nerves!

COLORED LIGHTS

from THE RINK

Words by FRED EBB
Music by JOHN KANDER

Copyright © 1983, 1985 by Kander & Ebb, Inc.
All Rights Controlled and Administered by Bro 'N Sis Music Inc.
International Copyright Secured   All Rights Reserved
Used by Permission

37

Waltz tempo

Thump - ing "oom - pah - pah" _____ or - gan sound. _____

_____ Nois - y boys,

long and lean; gig - gles of girls in the

mez - za - nine; _____

Moderately slow

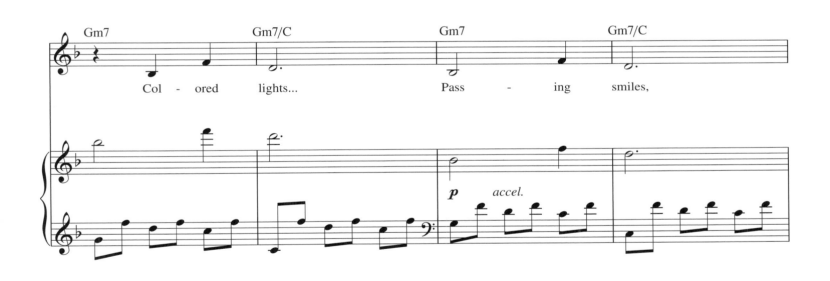

Col - ored   lights...   Pass - ing   smiles,

'round   and   'round.   Thump - ing   "oom - pah - pah"

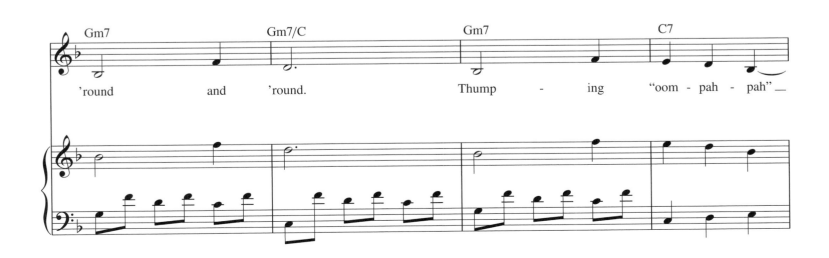

44

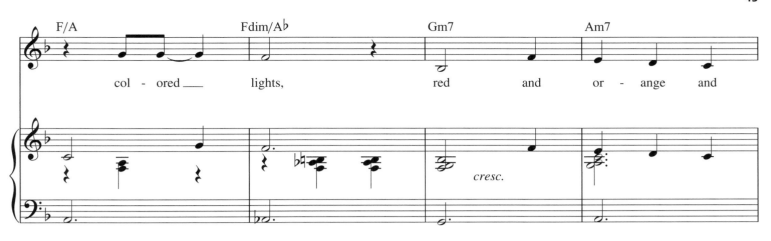

col - ored ___ lights, red and or - ange and

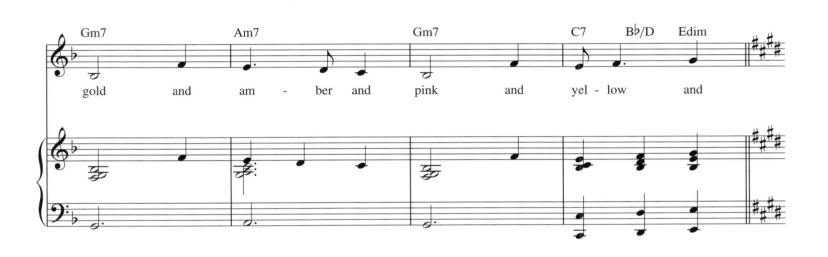

gold and am - ber and pink and yel - low and

green. ___

B7 D#m7(b5)/C# D#dim

E6

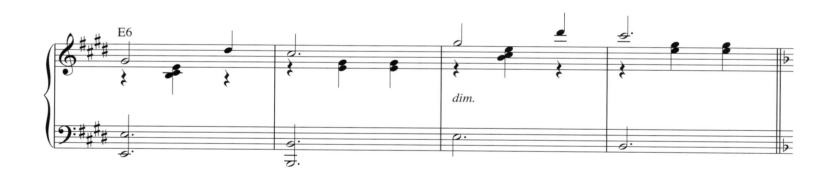

dim.

Slower

F/C   F6/C   Fmaj7/C   F6/C

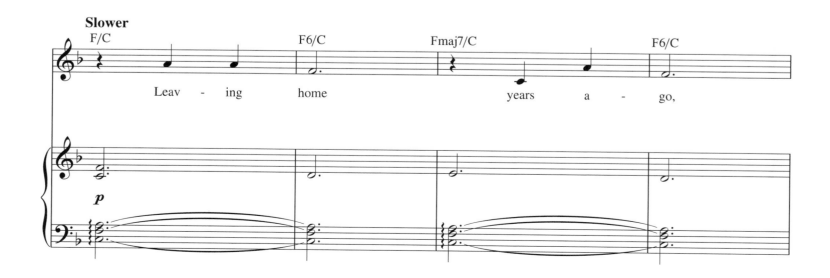

Leav - ing home   years a - go,

p

LIZA WITH A "Z"

Words by FRED EBB
Music by JOHN KANDER

Copyright © 1966, 1974 by Alley Music Corp. and Trio Music Company
Copyright Renewed
International Copyright Secured   All Rights Reserved
Used by Permission

"Z" in-stead of "S", "Lie" in-stead of "Lee". It's sim-ple as can be, see:

Even faster

Li - za. Then M I dou-ble N, then E dou-ble L I; you

dou - ble up the N, that's NN, not Noo. Then E dou-ble the L,

end it with an I. That's the way you say "Min -

LOSING MY MIND

from FOLLIES

Music and Lyrics by
STEPHEN SONDHEIM

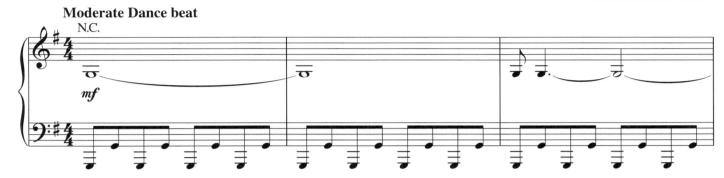

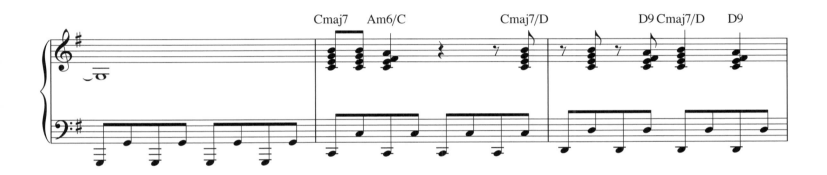

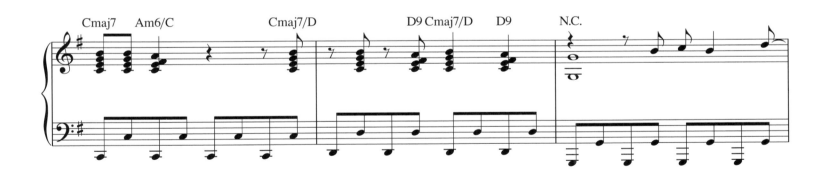

Copyright © 1971 by Range Road Music Inc., Jerry Leiber Music, Mike Stoller Music, Rilting Music, Inc. and Burthen Music Co., Inc.
Copyright Renewed
All Rights Administered by Herald Square Music, Inc.
International Copyright Secured   All Rights Reserved
Used by Permission

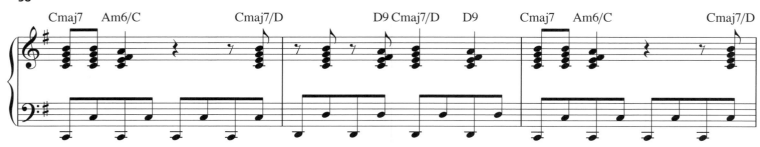

The sun   comes up; ____   I think _ a - bout   you.   The cof - fee   cup; ____
The morn - ing ends; ____   I think _ a - bout   you.   I talk to   friends; _

(loco)

__   I think _ a - bout   you.   I want you   so, ____ it's like I'm los - ing   my
__   I think _ a - bout   you.   And do they   know? _ It's like I'm los - ing   my

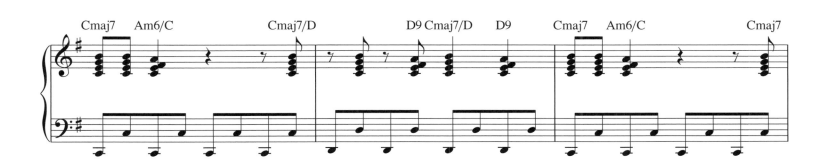

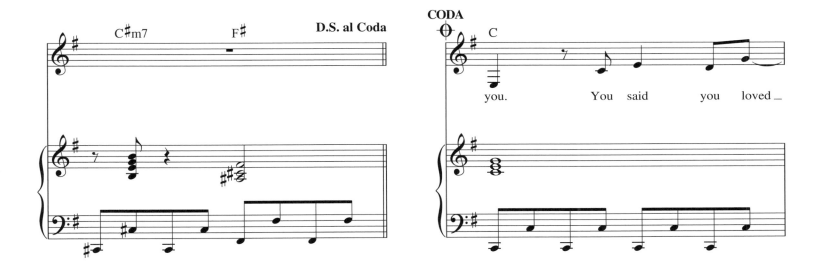

MAYBE THIS TIME
from the Musical CABARET

Words by FRED EBB
Music by JOHN KANDER

Copyright © 1963, 1972 by Alley Music Corp. and Trio Music Company
Copyright Renewed
International Copyright Secured   All Rights Reserved
Used by Permission

gin. _____ It's ___ gon - na

hap - pen, ___ hap - pen some - time. ___ May - be

this time, ___ may - be this time ___ I'll win. _____

(loco)

ME AND MY BABY

from CHICAGO

Words by FRED EBB
Music by JOHN KANDER

Bright Two-beat

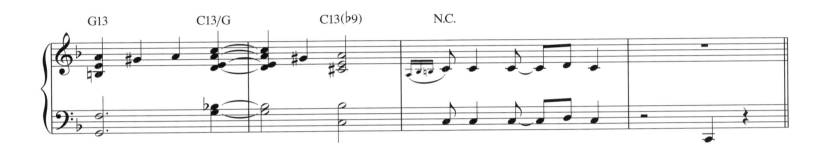

Me and my ba - by, my ba - by and me; _____

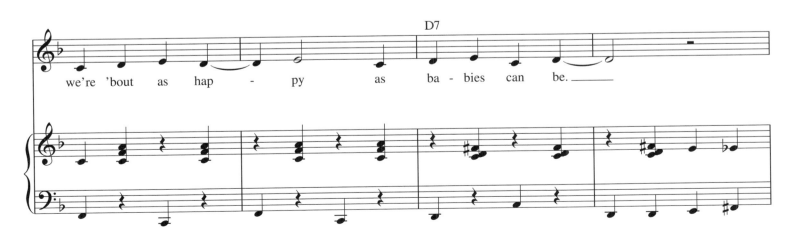

we're 'bout as hap - py as ba - bies can be. _____

Copyright © 1974, 1975 by Unichappell Music Inc. and Kander & Ebb, Inc.
Copyright Renewed
All Rights Administered by Unichappell Music Inc.
International Copyright Secured   All Rights Reserved

Look at my ba - by, my ba - by and me. _____ A

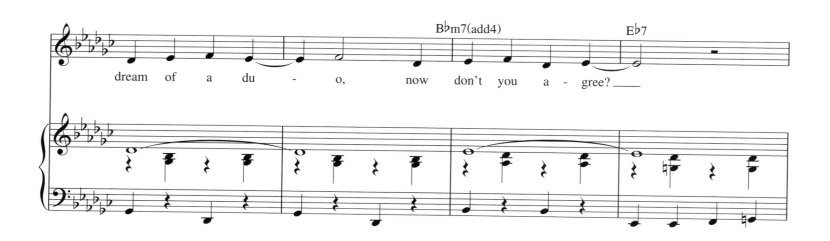

dream of a du - o, now don't you a - gree? _____

Why keep it mum _____ when there's noth - ing to hide? _____ And

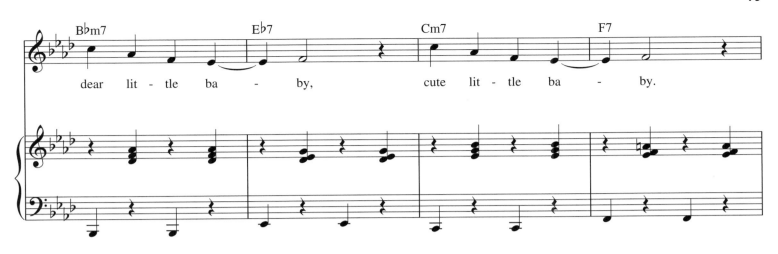

dear lit - tle ba - by, cute lit - tle ba - by.

Look at _____ my ba - by _____ and

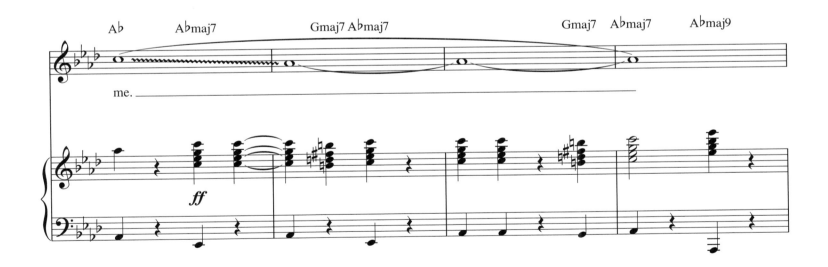

me. _____

Swing (Half tempo)

MEIN HERR
from the Musical CABARET

Words by FRED EBB
Music by JOHN KANDER

Copyright © 1972 by Alley Music Corp. and Trio Music Company
Copyright Renewed
International Copyright Secured   All Rights Reserved
Used by Permission

MONEY, MONEY
from the Musical CABARET

Words by FRED EBB
Music by JOHN KANDER

Moderately bright

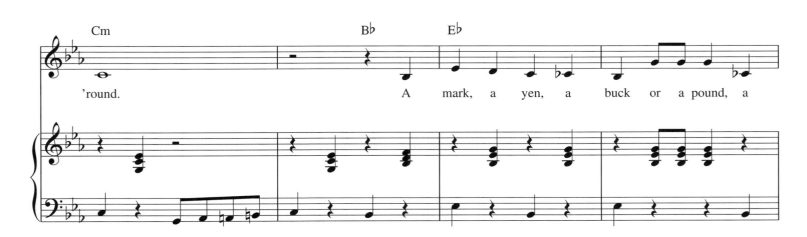

Copyright © 1972 by Alley Music Corp. and Trio Music Company
Copyright Renewed
International Copyright Secured   All Rights Reserved
Used by Permission

buck or a pound, a buck or a pound is all that makes the world go a-round, that

clink - ing, clank - ing sound can make the world go 'round.

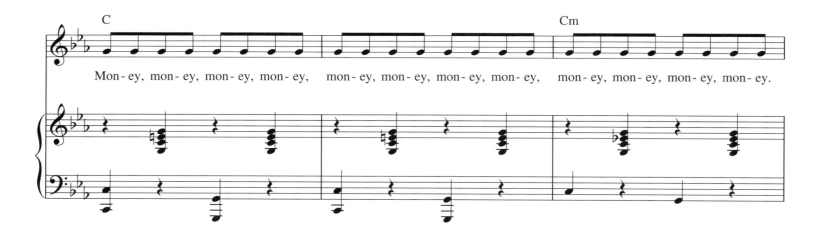

Mon - ey, mon - ey, mon - ey, mon - ey, mon - ey, mon - ey, mon - ey, mon - ey, mon - ey, mon - ey, mon - ey, mon - ey.

If you hap - pen to be rich, and you feel like a night's en - ter-tain - ment, you can

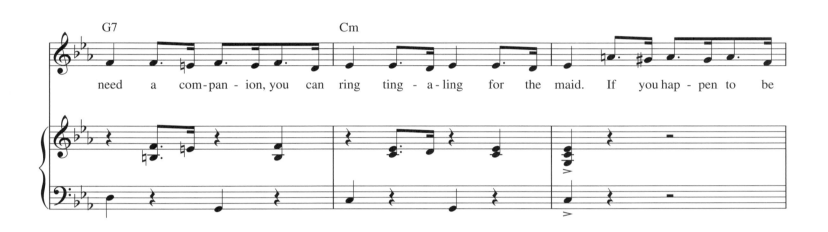

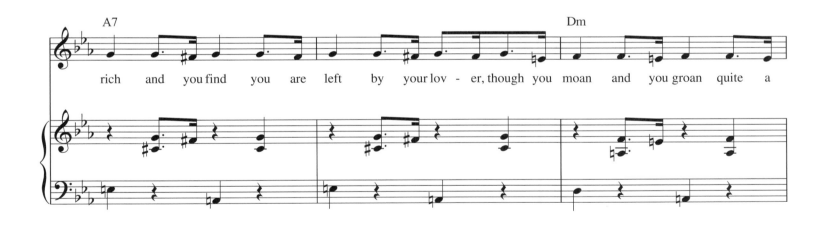

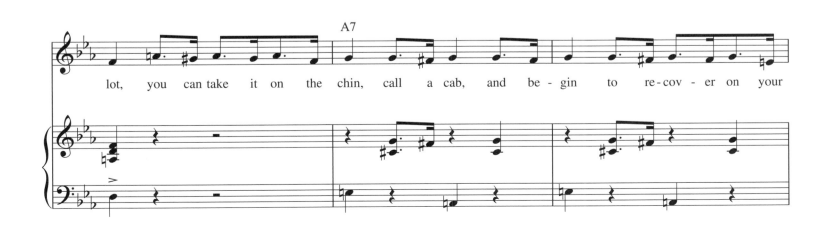

mon-ey, mon-ey, mon-ey, mon-ey, mon. When you have-n't an - y coal in the stove and you

freeze in the win - ter and you curse to the wind at your fate. When you have-n't an - y

shoes on your feet and your coat's thin as pa - per and you look thir - ty pounds un-der-

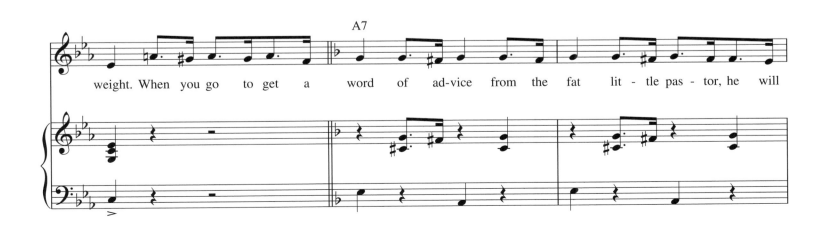

weight. When you go to get a word of ad-vice from the fat lit - tle pas - tor, he will

tell you to love ev - er - more. But when hu - ger comes to rap, rat - a - tat, rat - a -

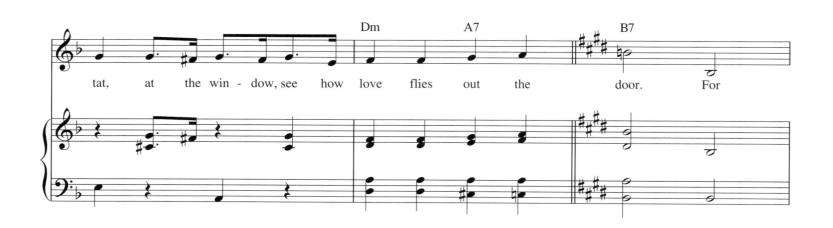

tat, at the win - dow, see how love flies out the door. For

mon - ey makes the world go a - round, the world go a - round, the world go a - round.

Mon - ey makes the world go a - round, the clink - ing, clank - ing

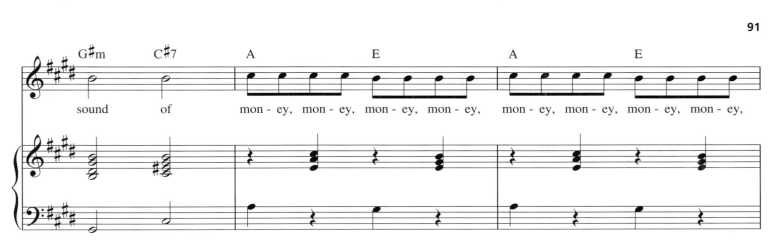

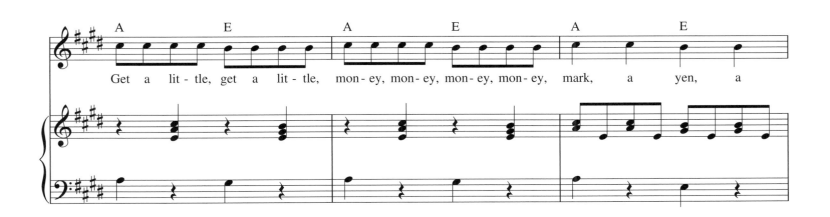

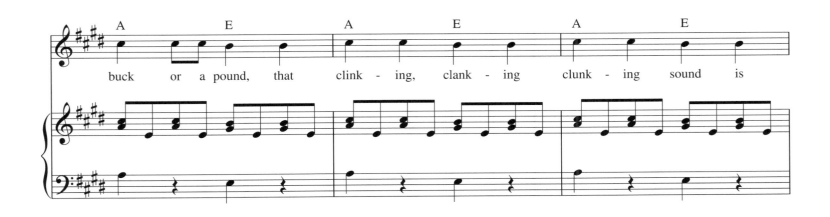

MONEY TREE

Words by FRED EBB
Music by JOHN KANDER

Copyright © 1977 by Unichappell Music Inc. and Kander & Ebb, Inc.
Copyright Renewed
All Rights Administered by Unichappell Music Inc.
International Copyright Secured   All Rights Reserved

MY OWN BEST FRIEND

from CHICAGO

Words by FRED EBB
Music by JOHN KANDER

Copyright © 1973, 1975 by Unichappell Music Inc. and Kander & Ebb, Inc.
Copyright Renewed
All Rights Administered by Unichappell Music Inc.
International Copyright Secured   All Rights Reserved

MY OWN SPACE

Words by FRED EBB
Music by JOHN KANDER

Copyright © 1977 by Unichappell Music Inc. and Kander & Ebb, Inc.
Copyright Renewed
All Rights Administered by Unichappell Music Inc.
International Copyright Secured   All Rights Reserved

THEME FROM
"NEW YORK, NEW YORK"

from NEW YORK, NEW YORK

Words by FRED EBB
Music by JOHN KANDER

Moderate Swing

Start spread-in' the news. I'm leav-in' to-day. I want to be a part ___ of it, New York, New York.

© 1977 (Renewed) UNITED ARTISTS CORPORATION
All Rights Controlled by EMI UNART CATALOG INC. (Publishing) and ALFRED PUBLISHING CO., INC. (Print)
All Rights Reserved   Used by Permission

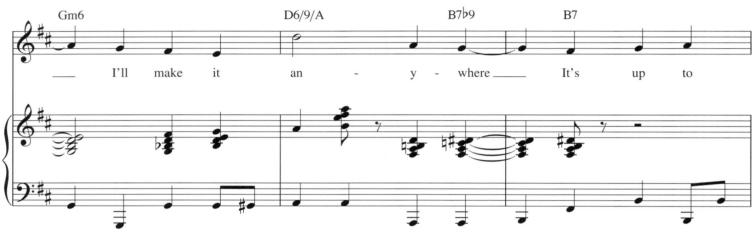

NOWADAYS

from CHICAGO

Words by FRED EBB
Music by JOHN KANDER

This song is a duet for Velma and Roxie in the show, adapted here as a solo.

Copyright © 1975 by Unichappell Music Inc. and Kander & Ebb, Inc.
Copyright Renewed
All Rights Administered by Unichappell Music Inc.
International Copyright Secured   All Rights Reserved

A QUIET THING

from FLORA, THE RED MENACE

Words by FRED EBB
Music by JOHN KANDER

Copyright © 1965 by Alley Music Corp. and Trio Music Company
Copyright Renewed
International Copyright Secured   All Rights Reserved
Used by Permission

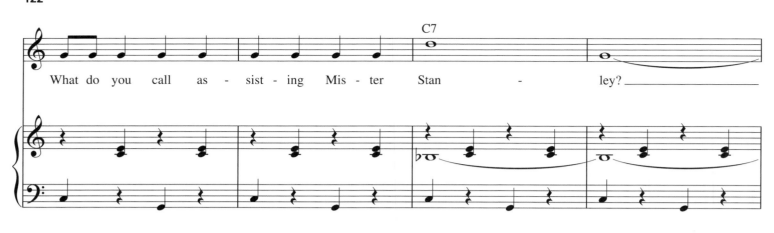

What do you call as - sist - ing Mis - ter Stan - ley? _____

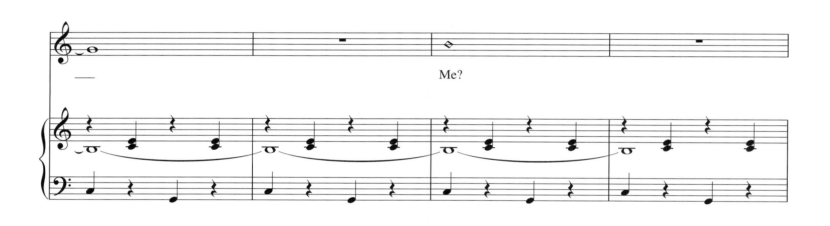

_ Me?

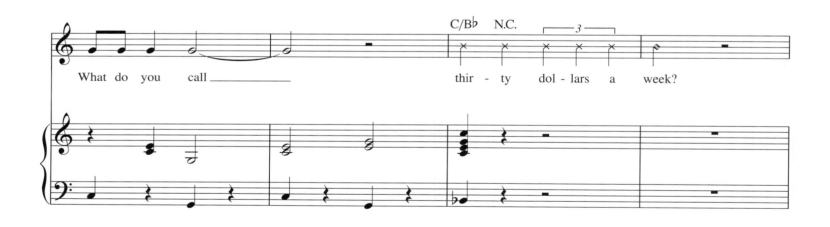

What do you call _____ thir - ty dol - lars a week?

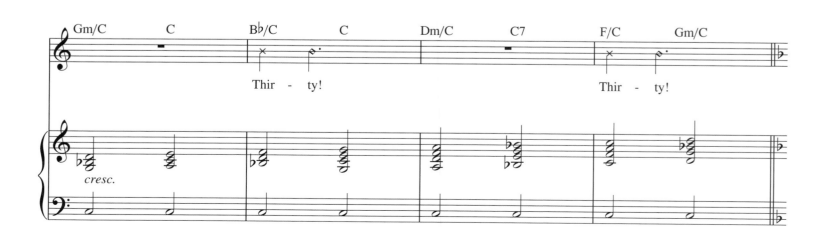

Thir - ty! Thir - ty!

cresc.

RING THEM BELLS

Words and Music by FRED EBB
and JOHN KANDER

Copyright © 1970 by Alley Music Corp. and Trio Music Company
Copyright Renewed
International Copyright Secured All Rights Reserved
Used by Permission

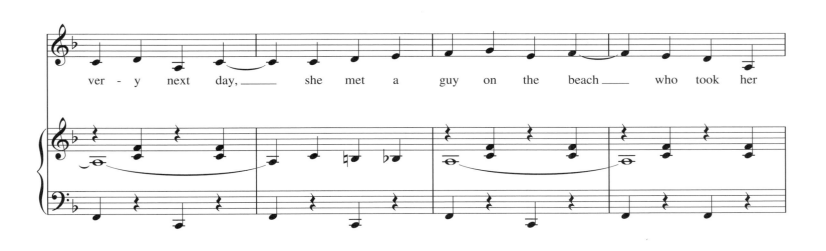

She met a | And so, she went to Du - brov - nik, and the

ver - y next day, ____ she met a guy on the beach ____ who took her

rea - son a - way. ____ Yes, it was love at first sight, ____ and quite a

was-n't e-nough,___ poor Shir-ley thought she'd gone deaf,___ when he told her his a-part-ment there was Twen-ty-nine F!___

Yes, she was 'E', he was 'F',___

SARA LEE

Words by FRED EBB
Music by JOHN KANDER

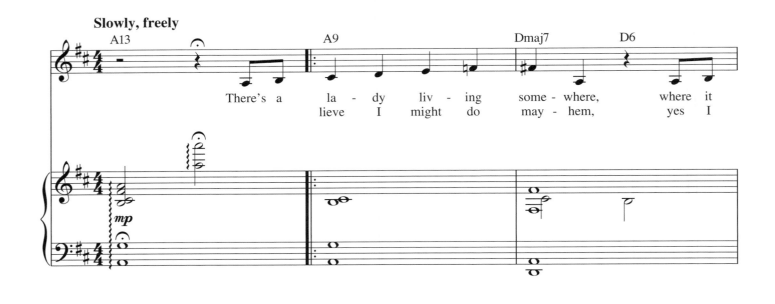

Slowly, freely

There's a la-dy liv-ing some-where, where it
lieve I might do may-hem, yes I

is I do not know, but I long to write and
might de-stroy my-self, if I ev-er found her

tell her that I love her so. _____ I be-
miss-ing from my gro-cer's

Copyright © 1965 by Alley Music Corp. and Trio Music Company
Copyright Renewed
International Copyright Secured   All Rights Reserved
Used by Permission

SHINE IT ON

Words by FRED EBB
Music by JOHN KANDER

Copyright © 1977 by Unichappell Music Inc. and Kander & Ebb, Inc.
Copyright Renewed
All Rights Administered by Unichappell Music Inc.
International Copyright Secured   All Rights Reserved

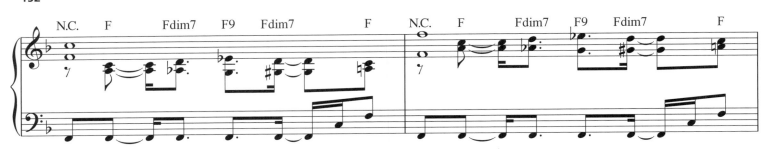

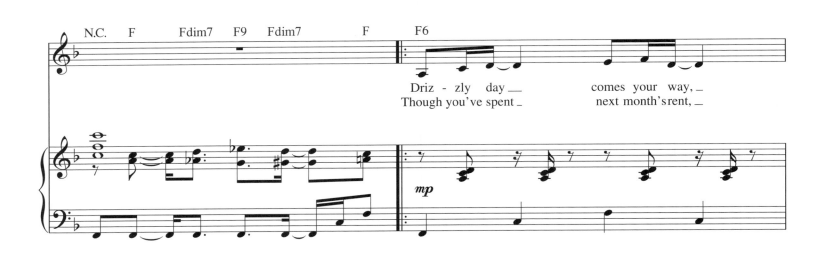

Driz - zly day __ comes your way, __
Though you've spent __ next month's rent, __

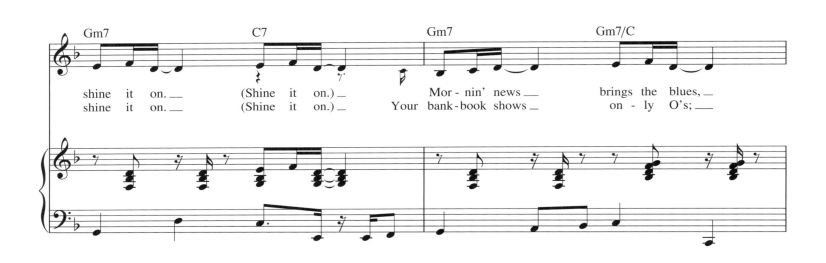

shine it on. __ (Shine it on.) __ Mor - nin' news __ brings the blues, __
shine it on. __ (Shine it on.) __ Your bank-book shows __ on - ly O's; __

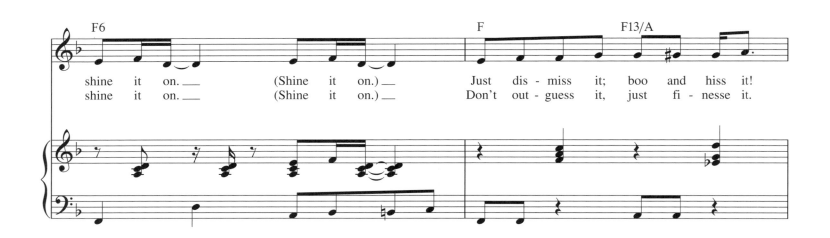

shine it on. __ (Shine it on.) __ Just dis - miss it; boo and hiss it!
shine it on. __ (Shine it on.) __ Don't out - guess it, just fi - nesse it.

SING HAPPY
from FLORA, THE RED MENACE

Words by FRED EBB
Music by JOHN KANDER

Copyright © 1965 by Alley Music Corp. and Trio Music Company
Copyright Renewed
International Copyright Secured   All Rights Reserved
Used by Permission

THE SINGER

Written by
WALTER MARKS

Moderate Two-beat

In a small ca - fé, _____ on a crowd - ed night, _____ in a spot of light _____ stands the sing - er.

e - vil crowd _____ hangs on ev - 'ry word, _____ but the sounds are slurred _____ by the sing - er, Then the till the

© 1970 (Renewed 1998) FRED AHLERT MUSIC GROUP (ASCAP)/Administered by BUG MUSIC
All Rights Reserved   Used by Permission

STEPPING OUT – MAIN TITLE

from STEPPING OUT

Words by FRED EBB
Music by JOHN KANDER

Moderate Soft-shoe tempo

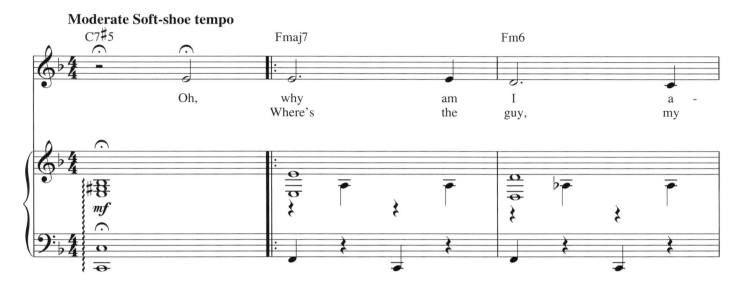

Oh, why am I a -
Where's the guy, my

lone to - night, when I should
Mis - ter Right, who might take

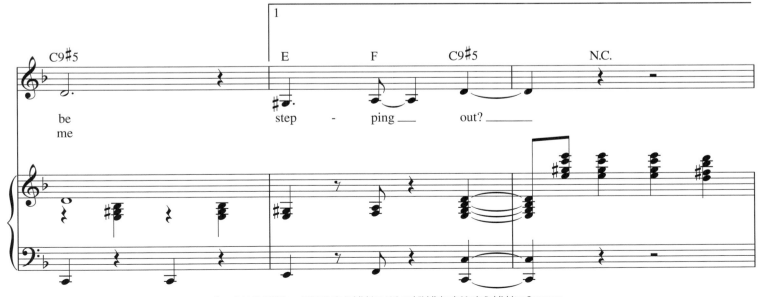

be step - ping out?
me

Copyright © 1992 Sony/ATV Music Publishing LLC and Fiddleback Music Publishing Company
All Rights on behalf of Sony/ATV Music Publishing LLC Administered by Sony/ATV Music Publishing LLC, 8 Music Square West, Nashville, TN 37203
International Copyright Secured   All Rights Reserved

Am7
D13
D7♯5
D7
G13
Wait and
C13
E
F
E♭maj7/F
Cm9
F7♯5
see; there's no doubt.
B♭maj7
B♭m6
F(add9)/A
I've played the fool in love's emp - ty
G13
Gm7
Gm9
pool, but now, now,

TAKING A CHANCE ON LOVE

Words by JOHN LA TOUCHE
and TED FETTER
Music by VERNON DUKE

© 1940 (Renewed) EMI MILLER CATALOG INC.
All Rights Controlled and Administered by EMI MILLER CATALOG INC. (Publishing) and ALFRED PUBLISHING CO., INC. (Print)
All Rights Reserved   Used by Permission

THERE WHEN I NEED HIM

Words by FRED EBB
Music by JOHN KANDER

Slowly and very freely

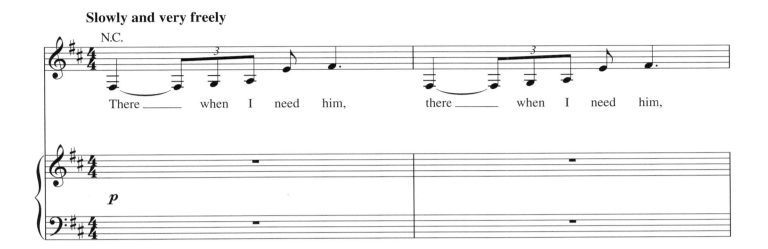

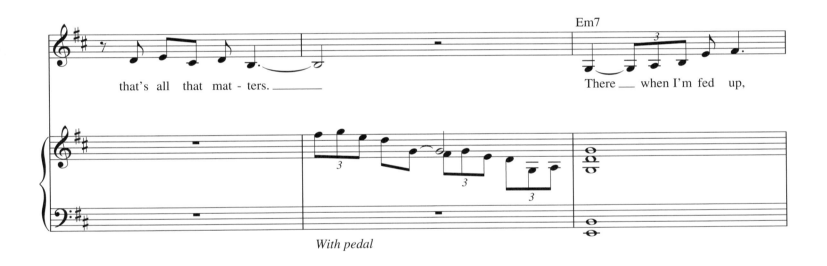

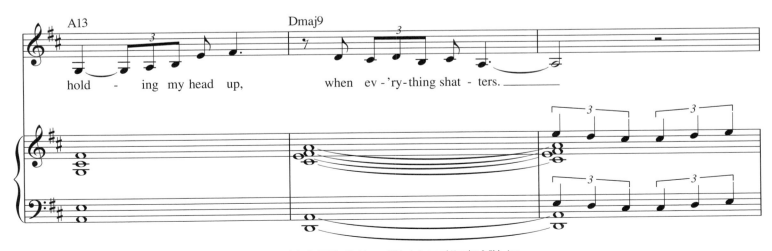

Copyright © 1977 by Unichappell Music Inc. and Kander & Ebb, Inc.
Copyright Renewed
All Rights Administered by Unichappell Music Inc.
International Copyright Secured   All Rights Reserved